DR. TEA TIME

Written by **Jody Singh**
Illustrated by **Rifai Suhganda**

This book is dedicated to my dad who was the first person to teach me the the skills to have the best bedside manner and to Dr. Sugiyama who has the best bedside manner in the whole wide world.

This Book Belongs To

_____

This is Dr. Tea. He wears a
bow tie, glasses, a lab coat.

He has lived at Bedside Manor his whole life and he loves helping everyone in the town.

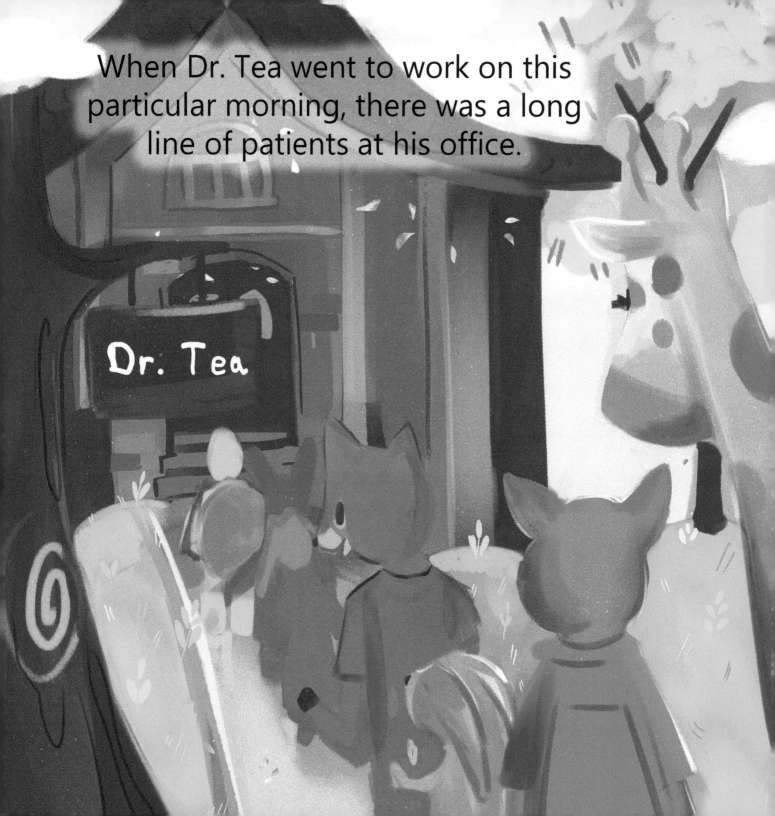

When Dr. Tea went to work on this particular morning, there was a long line of patients at his office.

Dr. Tea calls for his first patient, Terry the turtle.

Dr. Tea said, 'but you should celebrate that you take your time because that allows you to enjoy everything around you. That is called being **PRESENT**.

Next patient is Jerome the Giraffe. He is worried because he is the tallest in his school.

Dr Tea says, "it is okay, Burt, lots of us have bald spots."

Then Dr. Tea shows Burt his bald spots. Burt is **CONFIDENT**.

Andy the alligator has a tummy ache and thinks he may have appendicitis.

It turns out Andy is just nervous. Knowing that he is okay makes him feel better. Andy is **CALM**.

Dan the dolphin has diarrhea, and no one will swim with him.

Tom the Pterodactyl feels like everyone is making fun of him because they keep telling him his pee is silent.

Sloane
the sloth
says they
are feeling
stressed.

Dr. Tea prescribes mindfulness. Dr. Tea asks Sloane to take a deep breath in and then breathe out and reminds Sloane how beautiful they are. Sloane is being **MINDFUL**.

Monroe the monkey is feeling funky. He is fine. He just wanted to show Dr. Tea his dance moves. Monroe is **JOYFUL**.

Dr. Tea gives Freddy a noisemaker so every time he is about to fart, he can distract everyone with a funny sound. Freddy is HUMOUR.

So Dr. Tea brought everyone together into the waiting room.

Andy says, "I love his soft hair because it is so different than mine".

Dr. Tea asks Sloane, 'what is something you love about Jerome?

I love that he can describe things we cannot see, and it makes the world more beautiful.

I love that
he is so
confident,
and he does
not care what
others think.

Dr. Tea says that he is so proud of everyone finding the positive in everyone.

Dr. Tea realized no one was sick in his office today and reminded everyone to celebrate their differences because it makes the world so beautiful.

So today, my prescription for everyone is to go out and spread your loving-kindness and show the world how beautiful you are inside and out.
- Dr. Tea is **CARING**.

CPSIA information can be obtained
at www.ICGtesting.com
Printed in the USA
BVHW021400270622
640734BV00005B/5